Dolphin Ride

by Jill Atkins and Geraldine Rodriguez

"Will we see some dolphins today, Dad?"

asked Lexi.

"I hope so," said Dad.

"So do I," grinned Lexi, looking down

into the water. She loved dolphins.

Just then, there was a big splash

at the side of the boat.

"That made me jump!" laughed Dad.

Lexi watched as the dolphins swam

under the boat and leapt out of the water.

"They're so clever," she said.

Then, one of the dolphins swam up to the boat.

It looked at Lexi.

Lexi thought she saw the dolphin wink at her.

"I wish I could ride on your back,"

she said to the dolphin.

She closed her eyes and held her breath,

waiting for the dolphin to make another splash.

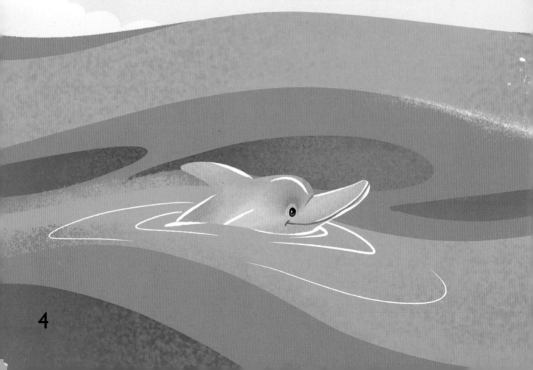

Lexi could taste the salty seawater.

As she stood and waited to feel the splash,

she thought about the dolphin.

Was it really looking at her?

Suddenly, Lexi felt herself speeding through the water. She opened her eyes.

"My wish has come true," she laughed as she held onto the dolphin's fin.

Soon they came to a ship.

It was the biggest ship that Lexi had ever seen.

The people standing on the decks waved at her.

"That looks fun!" they called. "Hold on tight."

"I will," said Lexi, waving back at them.

Then a fishing boat floated by.

"Keep away from that net!" cried Lexi.

"We don't want to get trapped."

The dolphin turned away from the fishing net

just in time.

Lexi held on to the dolphin's fin.

Suddenly, Lexi felt the dolphin slow down.

It had seen something out at sea.

Then Lexi saw it too.

There was another, bigger fin

and it was getting closer.

"Shark!" she yelled.

The shark followed them.

The dolphin swam as fast as it could.

Faster and faster it raced.

Lexi had to hold on very tight to stop herself falling off.

Soon the shark could not keep up.

Just when they thought they were

out of danger, a dark shadow fell over them.

An enormous tanker was sailing

towards them, making waves on each side.

"Look out!" shouted Lexi.

A big wave swept towards them.

Lexi tried to hang on to the dolphin's back

but the wave washed her off.

Lexi closed her eyes and held her breath.

Lexi opened her eyes. She wasn't in the water.

She was safe, sitting next to Dad.

"Dad! Dad! I had a ride on a dolphin!" Lexi said.

"We saw a ship and a fishing boat.

There was a shark and an enormous tanker.

But then I fell into the water ..."

Lexi stopped.

Dad smiled. "Well you're safe now," he said.

"Did I really have a dolphin ride?"

Lexi wondered.

Just at that moment, a dolphin swam

up to the boat.

Lexi thought she saw it wink at her.

Story order

Look at these 5 pictures and captions.
Put the pictures in the right order
to retell the story.

1

Lexi thought about the dolphin.

2

Lexi told Dad about her dolphin ride.

3

The big wave washed Lexi off.

4

Lexi and her dad spotted some dolphins.

5

Lexi rode on the dolphin's back.

Independent Reading

This series is designed to provide an opportunity for your child to read on their own. These notes are written for you to help your child choose a book and to read it independently.

In school, your child's teacher will often be using reading books which have been banded to support the process of learning to read. Use the book band colour your child is reading in school to help you make a good choice. *Dolphin Ride* is a good choice for children reading at Gold Band in their classroom to read independently.

The aim of independent reading is to read this book with ease, so that your child enjoys the story and relates it to their own experiences.

About the book

Lexi and her dad are on a boat trip. When they spot some dolphins, Lexi makes a wish to ride on a dolphin's back. Then she is suddenly on a magical dolphin ride! When a wave knocks her off, she is magically back with Dad. Did it really happen?

Before reading

Help your child to learn how to make good choices by asking:
"Why did you choose this book? Why do you think you will enjoy it?"
Look at the cover together and ask: "What do you think the story will be about?" Ask your child to think of what they already know about dolphins. Ask: "Do you think the girl is really on a dolphin ride?"
Remind your child that they can sound out the letters to make a word if they get stuck.
Decide together whether your child will read the story independently or read it aloud to you.

During reading

Remind your child of what they know and what they can do independently. If reading aloud, support your child if they hesitate or ask for help by telling the word. If reading to themselves, remind your child that they can come and ask for your help if stuck.

After reading

Support comprehension by asking your child to tell you about the story. Use the story order puzzle to encourage your child to retell the story in the right sequence, in their own words. The correct sequence can be found on the next page.

Help your child think about the messages in the book that go beyond the story and ask: "Do you think that Lexi really went on a dolphin ride? Why / why not?"

Give your child a chance to respond to the story: "If you could have a wish come true, what would it be?"

Extending learning

Help your child reflect on the story, by asking: "Have you ever had a day dream? Did your day dream feel like it had really happened?"

In the classroom, your child's teacher may be teaching suffixes. There are some examples in this book (+er, +est) that you could look at with your child: *biggest, bigger, closer, faster*. Find these together and ask your child to find the root word. Can they add a different suffix to change between the comparative (+er) to the superlative (+est)? Point out that sometimes the last letter of the root word is doubled before adding the suffix.

Franklin Watts
First published in Great Britain in 2018
by The Watts Publishing Group

Series Editors: Jackie Hamley and Melanie Palmer
Series Advisors: Dr Sue Bodman and Glen Franklin
Series Designer: Peter Scoulding

A CIP catalogue record for this book is
available from the British Library.

ISBN 978 1 4451 6253 9 (hbk)
ISBN 978 1 4451 6255 3 (pbk)
ISBN 978 1 4451 6254 6 (library ebook)

Printed in China

Franklin Watts
An imprint of
Hachette Children's Group
Part of The Watts Publishing Group
Carmelite House
50 Victoria Embankment
London EC4Y 0DZ

An Hachette UK Company
www.hachette.co.uk

www.franklinwatts.co.uk

FSC
www.fsc.org
MIX
Paper from
responsible sources
FSC® C104740

Answer to Story order: 4, 1, 5, 3, 2